Satellites

Reading
and
Language
Skills Book

When you see this symbol it means you will need a copy of the book.

Heinemann

Contents

* Children will need to read the whole story/play before doing these activities.

Finding Evidence

Answer these questions using evidence from the text.

1 What does Butch say that tells us he is a tough crook? (page 6)

2 How do we know that Chad is scared? (page 6)

3 What does Griffin say or do that tells us he is worried about Elliot? (page 9)

4 Why doesn't Sal want to take Elliot to the hospital? (page 10)

5 How does Paul try to persuade Griffin to help Elliot? (page 15)

6 How do we know Elliot is getting worse? (page 16)

7 Why does Griffin take Paul into the living room? (page 18)

8 Why does Griffin thank Paul? (page 23)

Active and Passive Verbs

Verbs are **active** when the subject of the sentence **does the action**.

e.g. *The car hit Elliot.*

subject   active verb

Verbs are **passive** when the subject of the sentence **has the action done to it**.

e.g. ***Elliot was hit** by the car.*

subject   passive verb

A **Write out the sentences underlining the verbs.**
Write whether the verbs are active or passive.

1   The boys were captured by the gang.   *passive*

2   The gang captured the boys.   *active*

3   The boys were watched by Sal.

4   Sal watched the boys.

5   Griffin opened the window.

6   The window was opened by Griffin.

7   Butch attacked Griffin.

8   Griffin was attacked by Butch.

B **Write a sentence of your own with an active verb,**
then rewrite the sentence making the verb passive.

Summarising the Play

A summary contains only the main points of a story.
Write a summary of each Act in Hostages.

Act 1

1   Two robbers enter the Chadwick's house.

2   They force Mrs Chadwick and the children into the living room.

3   Mrs Chadwick answers the …

Act 2

1   Mr Chadwick comes home …

2

3

Act 3

1   Inside the bank, the robbers …

2

3

5

Punctuation

Write out the sentences below, adding the missing punctuation from the box. You don't need to add speech marks as the text is from a play.

question mark	capital letter	full stop
comma		exclamation mark

1   has jake's sight been any better

2   does my dad owe you money

3   hey What's going on? what are you doing with that boy

4   i'll stop him You call the police

5   don't worry sir

6   really How exactly did the crash happen

7   Can I speak to mr roberts please

8   please come with me mr roberts to sign some papers.

9   Stop Stand still! you're under arrest

10   i made sure he would never get a job as a driver again

Find the Words

Look at the word square below. How many words can you find with four letters or more? The words can go in any direction but the squares must be touching.

Hint: find a letter string, e.g. -ight, -ould, and then search for words.

n	f	g	b	t
r	i	a	h	b
h	s	n	t	a
o	c	d	c	k
w	u	l	d	e

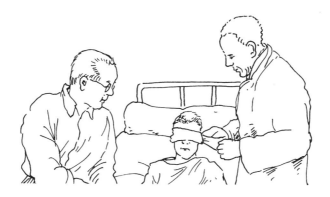

Prefixes and Their Meanings

A *Choose the correct meaning from the box for each prefix.*

self	between	~~water~~	above	not	below

Prefix	Meaning	Prefix	Meaning
hydro-	water	over-	
inter-		un-	
sub-		auto-	

B *Copy and complete the chart below. Use your work from above and a dictionary to help you fill in the missing meanings.*

Word	Meaning
autobiography	a book about oneself
autograph	
interval	a gap between two parts of a concert
intersect	
subway	a way under the ground
submarine	
overcoat	a coat you put on top of clothes
overhead	
unsure	not sure
unpleasant	

A Play Scene

A **Read through pages 15–19 of A Christmas Carol. Write the scene as a playscript:**

- think of a title for your scene

- set the scene by describing what is happening

- write the characters' speeches.

Title:

Set the scene:
Scrooge is …
The ghost of Jacob Marley is …

Scrooge *(With a trembling voice) What do you want with me?*

Marley *(Pointing his finger at Scrooge) Don't you …*

Scrooge *…*

B **Read your play scene with a friend.**

Old Language

A Christmas Carol *was written over one hundred years ago. Some of the language is very old-fashioned. Write these sentences as you would expect people to say them today.*

1   Are you the spirit whose coming was foretold?
    Are you the ghost I was told to expect?

2   Rise and walk with me.

3   Quick! My time grows short.

4   Show me no more, Spirit.

5   Take me where you will, Spirit.

6   We must be charitable and drink his health.

7   What's to become of his money?

8   What do you mean by coming here at this time of day?

Verbs

A **Read Chapter One of A Christmas Carol. Can you find eight action verbs? Set out your work in a spider diagram like this.**

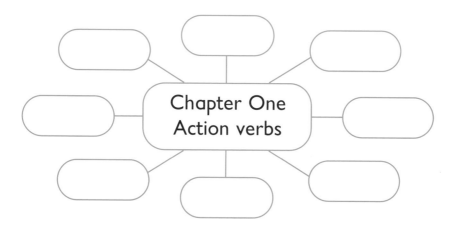

Chapter One
Action verbs

B **Write out these sentences, replacing the underlined verbs with your own more powerful verbs.**

1 Scrooge <u>walked</u> back to his office.

2 The ghost <u>came</u> through the locked door.

3 Scrooge <u>said</u> Christmas was a humbug.

4 Scrooge <u>asked</u> the spirit to stop showing him the past.

5 Scrooge <u>took</u> the spirit's cap and put it over the spirit's head.

Conjunctions

> **Conjunctions** are words which can join phrases, clauses or sentences together.
>
> e.g. Scrooge counted his money. He put it in a bag
> Scrooge counted his money **before** he put it in a bag.

Each pair of sentences below can be joined by a conjunction to make one sentence. List all the conjunctions from the box which could be used to join each pair.

and	then	and then	because	when
after	until	before	as	so

1   Bob Cratchit worked hard.   *then, and then, until, before*
    He went home.

2   The spirit showed Scrooge his past.
    He had once been happy.

3   Scrooge went with the spirit.
    He saw many poor people.

4   Scrooge felt sad.
    Tiny Tim was very ill.

5   The boy bought the turkey.
    Scrooge gave him half a crown.

6   Scrooge wished everyone a Merry Christmas.
    He went to see Fred.

Old Words and New Words

The sentences below use old-fashioned language. Find the old words, then choose the correct new words from the box to replace them.

over there	happy	three times	happy ghost
nothing	~~high~~	if only	frightening

1   He sat at a <u>lofty</u> desk.
    old word – lofty
    new word – high

2   Thrice the ghosts came to Scrooge.

3   Yonder lies the way.

4   Scrooge hung his head before the jolly spirit.

5   They had naught in the house.

6   Her jovial smile welcomed Bob Cratchit home.

7   The spirit had a fearsome form.

8   Wouldst that we had enough money.

Words Within Words

> One way to remember how to spell long words is to find smaller words within them.
>
> e.g. **newspapers** = *new, news, paper, papers, a, ape*

A **Write down all the small words you can find in these long words.**

business
nothing
gentlemen
tomorrow
bedclothes
another
understand
altogether

B **Draw the square below. Make a wordsearch for a friend using words from pages 55–58 of A Christmas Carol.**

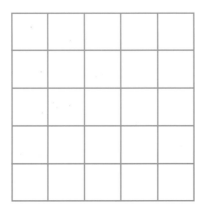

Writing a Blurb

> A **blurb** tells the reader just enough about a story to make them want to read the rest of it. It is usually on the back cover of the book.

Read this blurb for **Mountain Disaster.** *Then write your own blurb for* **Dive into Danger** *or* **Buried Alive!**

> ## Mountain Disaster
>
> Rob, Alex and Jenny are climbing the mountain when Alex falls and hits his head. Jenny stays with Alex while Rob goes back for help. But a mountain mist descends and Rob loses his way. Will he find his way back down the mountain in time to get help for Alex?

Remember:
- *don't give too much of the story away*
- *make the reader want to find out what happens.*

Spelling Mistakes

Jenny wrote a letter to a friend, telling him about the accident on the mountain. Can you spot fourteen spelling mistakes in her letter, and write out the words correctly?

Dear Paul,

We had a teribel time last week! Rob, Alex and I were climing in the mountains when Alex fell and cut his hed. I stayd with Alex while Rob went four help. Nobody came for ages, becuase Rob got lost in the missed. I new I should try to make Alex talk, but he wouldn't reply. I thort he was going to dye.

At last, Rob came back with some help, and soon the rescue helicopter arived. Alex had two go too hospital, but luckly he's all right now.

See you soon,

Jenny

Work with a partner to check the spellings in a dictionary. Test each other on the words.

What Kind of Text?

A **Read the text extracts below. Choose a text type from the box to describe each extract.**

| report | discussion | instructions | persuasion |

1 **Mountain Rescue Success!**
A boy was rescued yesterday after he fell and badly cut his head. His father described how he had gone with two friends to climb to the top of Mount Tor.

2 Dear Mum,
Tim went potholing last week and said it was great. Can I go? There is no danger as he has already been there.

3 **Rules for Mountain Climbers**
- Tell the warden where you are going.
- Take good waterproof clothes.
- Take emergency rations.

4 Some people say that travelling across a desert is dangerous but I think that if people are sensible and careful, there is no real danger.

B **Write the next sentence for each extract.**

Spelling Tricky Words

There are different ways to remember how to spell difficult words. Here are some examples.

Word	How to remember the spelling
believe	the word **lie** is in the middle of *belie*ve
Wednesday	break it up into syllables: **Wed – nes – day**
piece	make up a phrase: **a piece of pie** (the word **pie** is in *pie*ce)
because	make up a phrase using the letters of the word: **Big Elephants Can Always Use Small Elephants**

Choose ten words from the box below. Write how you will remember how to spell them.

across	surprise	beautiful	altogether
desperately	ceiling	interested	
suddenly	carefully	unconscious	friend
disappear	disbelief	tomorrow	
extremely	height	calendar	neighbour

18

More Conjunctions

Conjunctions are words which can join phrases, clauses or sentences together.
e.g. Adam and Jack went potholing **because** they enjoyed it.

Complete these sentences.

1   Jack wanted to explore the cave **because** …

2   Adam and Jack went into the cave **and** …

3   They heard a rumbling noise **but** …

4   Adam knew the cave **so** …

5   Jack prepared to dive into the hole **although** …

6   Adam and Jack escaped from the cave **before** …

How Did Ben Feel?

A **Read this extract from Buried Alive!**

> Ben hurried on, but the tracks had disappeared and he couldn't see where he was going. Then, in the distance, he saw the truck. Head down, eyes stinging, sand in his mouth, he staggered on. The truck was lying on its side with one back door open. Ben knew that if he could get inside the truck, he would have shelter. He pushed some of the sand aside and got in. Ben curled up, clutching his knees. He was shaking with fear.

The author creates a vivid picture of Ben caught in the sandstorm. Find six phrases in the extract which create this picture.
e.g. head down

B **How do you think Ben felt in the extract? Complete these sentences.**

1 When the tracks disappeared, Ben felt ...

2 When he saw the truck, he felt ...

3 When he was inside the truck, he felt ...

Writing a Book Review

Write a review of **No-Luck Holmes and the Case of the Missing Monarch** *for other Year 6 pupils. Use the frame to help you.*

Title:	No-Luck Holmes and the Case of the Missing Monarch
Authors:	
Illustrator:	
Publisher:	

1   The most amusing character is ... because ...

2   The funniest part of the story is when ...

3   The best illustration is ...
    This shows ...

4   I think this book would be enjoyed by ...

5   I would give this book ... out of 10.

Plot Structure

Outline the plot of No-Luck Holmes and the Case of the Missing Monarch *for someone who has not read the story. Include the most important events and write no more than ten sentences.*

1   *No-Luck, the nephew of Sherlock Holmes, comes to work with Dr Watson.*

2   *Sherlock Holmes goes …*

3   *Queen Victoria …*

4   *Inspector Bone …*

Complex Sentences

A **clause** is a group of words in a sentence which has a verb. **Complex sentences** have more than one clause. The clauses are joined by **connectives.**

1st clause

connective

e.g. No-Luck often made stupid suggestions **but**

he realised the Beefeater was Sherlock Holmes.

2nd clause

Complete the sentences below, using the connectives in the box to join the clauses.

but	so	when	because	until	then

1 Holmes was annoyed _____ No-Luck broke his precious vase.

2 No-Luck remembered to put his trousers on _____ he forgot to put on his vest and shirt.

3 Her Majesty was putting on her jewels, _____ one of the corgis ran in.

4 No-Luck and Watson followed Ratface _____ they could find the Queen.

5 Holmes pretended to be Sally the maid, _____ he pulled off his disguise.

6 Everyone thought Holmes had drowned _____ he had fallen into the sewer.

Sherlock's Plans

*Imagine you are Sherlock Holmes. Complete the sentences which list your plans throughout the story. Underline the words that show these sentences only suggest what you **might** do.*

1   <u>If</u> I kidnap the Queen, everyone will think …

2   I might make a fortune if …

3   I could ask Ratface Rogers to …

4   I wonder if Watson and my stupid nephew, No-Luck, will …

5   I could pretend to be the Queen's Maid and …

6   If I disguise myself as a Beefeater, then …

Proverbs

In the story, No-Luck says, "caviar doesn't grow on trees". This is a reference to the proverb 'money doesn't grow on trees', meaning that money is not easily come by.

Write out these proverbs with their correct meanings from the box below.

1 A new broom sweeps clean.

2 A stitch in time saves nine.

3 A wolf in sheep's clothing.

4 A cat may look at a king.

5 A watched pot never boils.

6 There's no smoke without fire.

- Things won't happen any sooner because you keep watching for them.
- Somebody dangerous is disguised as someone innocent.
- If you do something small now, it will save a big job later.
- There's usually a good reason for a rumour.
- Anyone can look at important people.
- A new boss will reorganise everything.

Prefixes, Suffixes and Roots

The **root** is the main part of a word.

Prefixes are joined onto the **front** of a word.

Suffixes are joined onto the **end** of a word.

re**turn**ing

prefix root suffix

You can make new words by changing the prefixes and suffixes.

e.g. turn ➔ re**turns**, turn**ed**

Copy and complete the chart. Write the root word and then write as many new words as you can by adding prefixes and suffixes.

Word	Root word	New words
player	play	players, playing, played, replay
hopping		
kidnapped		
amazement		
panicky		
undo		
outside		

Gemma's Point of View

A Write a summary of Creepy Kane from Gemma's point of view. Use the frame to help you.

1   I arrived at Kane's house.

2   Kane …

3   Auntie Chris arrived home.

4   That night …

5   It was not Zora but …

6   I saw …

7   I screamed and woke everyone up.

8   Kane had made …

9   I decided to …

B What part of the story can't you write about, if you are writing from Gemma's point of view? Why is this?

I can't write about the part where …

This is because …

Adding the Suffix 'y'

Look at the words in the box. What happens when -y is added to them? Can you sort the words into two groups?

creep ➔ creepy   jump ➔ jumpy   ease ➔ easy

smoke ➔ smoky   ice ➔ icy   noise ➔ noisy

laze ➔ lazy   sport ➔ sporty   paper ➔ papery

juice ➔ juicy   stone ➔ stony   snow ➔ snowy

craze ➔ crazy   luck ➔ lucky   cloud ➔ cloudy

milk ➔ milky   nose ➔ nosy   whisper ➔ whispery

Write a rule that will help you remember what happens when you add -y to words.

Writing a Review

Write a review of Knight of the Road *for a cycling* magazine. The readers are keen mountain bikers aged 10–13 years.

Your review should be no more than 100 words. You should include:

- what the story is about

- whether you think the story is true

- your conclusion. Is the story worth reading? You could give the story marks out of 10.

Start your review like this:

Knight of the Road is a story about a very special bike – Silver Knight. It belongs to Matt, but while he is away, his younger brother, Dan, takes it for a ride.

Punctuation

Write out the passage, putting in all the missing punctuation.

matt looked round as dan moved his bike to the grass and walked over to them

it was lucky wasnt it matt said softly if i hadnt stopped to have a moan at my little brother here he squeezed dans shoulder i know it was a fluke but you borrowing silver knight probably saved my life

dan didnt answer instead he turned and looked at silver knight he remembered matt saying that the bike was his best mate i look after silver knight and silver knight looks after me

Creating Similes

A **Look at the description of the alien on pages 52 and 53 of Crash Landing. Make up some similes to describe the alien.**

e.g. The creature was as big as my baby sister.

1   It had a head as huge as …

2   Its mouth was like …

3   Its eyes were like …

4   Its arm was as thin as a …

5   Its four fingers were like …

6   The suction pads on its fingers were like …

B **What do you think the alien thought of the boys? Write a simile to describe the boys from the alien's point of view.**

The boys were like …

Writing Reports

Imagine you are the army officer who spoke to the boys in the wood. You have to write two short reports.

The first report is for the local newspaper. Remember you don't want the public to know the truth. The second report is for the army. You should explain what really happened.

Newspaper Report

At 11.00 am we were called to investigate a crash in the woods. We arrived at 11.10 am and found ...

Army Report

At 11.00 we were alerted to a problem in the woods. At 11.10 we arrived at the scene to find ...